TABLE of CONTENTS

A MIDSUMMER NIGHT'S DREAM

RETOLD BY
NEL YOMTOV

ILLUSTRATED BY
BERENICE MUNIZ

COLOURED BY
FARES MAESE

Raintree

www.raintreepublishers.co.uk
Visit our website to find out
more information about
Raintree books.

To order:
☎ Phone 0845 6044371
▤ Fax +44 (0) 1865 312263
▣ Email myorders@raintreepublishers.co.uk

Customers from outside the UK please telephone +44 1865 312262

Raintree is an imprint of Capstone Global Library Limited, a company incorporated in
England and Wales having its registered office at 7 Pilgrim Street, London, EC4V 6LB –
Registered company number: 6695582

Text © Stone Arch Books 2012
First published in the United Kingdom by
Capstone Global Library Ltd in 2012
The moral rights of the proprietor have been asserted.

Art Director: Kay Fraser
Graphic Designer: Hilary Wacholz
Editor: Diyan Leake
Production Specialist: Victoria Fitzgerald
Originated by Capstone Global Library Ltd
Printed in and bound in China by South China Printing Company Ltd

ISBN 978 1 406 24326 0
16 15 14 13 12
10 9 8 7 6 5 4 3 2 1

British Library Cataloguing in Publication Data
A full catalogue record for this book is available from the British Library.

SHAKESPEARE

WILLIAM SHAKESPEARE WAS ONE OF THE GREATEST WRITERS THE WORLD HAS EVER KNOWN.

HE WROTE COMEDIES, TRAGEDIES, HISTORIES, AND ROMANCES ABOUT ANCIENT HEROES, BRUTAL WARS, AND MAGICAL CREATURES.

THIS IS ONE OF THOSE STORIES . . .

THE COMEDY OF

A MIDSUMMER NIGHT'S DREAM

"The course of true love never did run smooth."

ACT ONE

Just then, Egeus, father of fair Hermia, enters Theseus's palace.

What news do you bring, Egeus?

I come with a complaint against my daughter, Hermia.

Demetrius has my consent to marry her . . .

But Lysander has tricked my child with lies!

He has turned my own daughter against me.

Meanwhile, at the home of Quince, several actors meet to rehearse a play that will be performed at Theseus and Hippolyta's wedding.

Our play is a sad comedy called *Pyramus and Thisbe*.

You, Nick Bottom, will play Pyramus, a lover who kills himself.

I will move the audience to storms of tears, Quince!

Flute, you will play the role of Thisbe, the lady that Pyramus loves.

But I have a beard!

Then you shall wear a mask.

ACT
TWO

"I am that merry
wanderer of the night."

"Remember when we saw a mermaid riding a dolphin's back?"

"Flying above, Cupid let loose an arrow from his bow . . ."

Puck, come listen . . .

"Missing its mark, it fell upon a flower."

THUNK!

When set on sleeping eyelids, the juice of that flower will make any man or woman fall madly in love with the next creature it sees.

Fetch me that flower, Puck.

When Titania is asleep, I'll drop the juice of the flower on her eyes.

The next thing she looks upon, she shall love!

And before I remove the spell . . .

I'll make her give the boy to me.

32

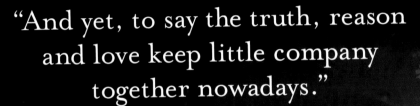

"And yet, to say the truth, reason and love keep little company together nowadays."

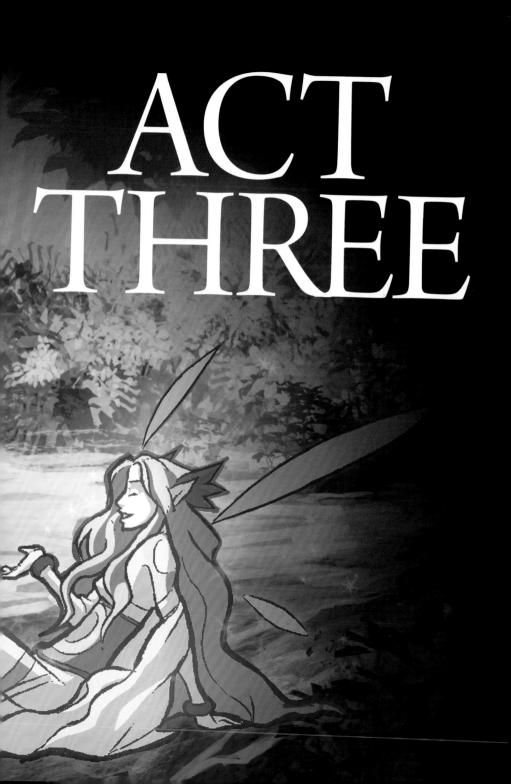

ACT THREE

Meanwhile, the actors meet in the woods. They do not see Titania sleeping nearby.

Quince, there are things in our comedy that must change.

First, Pyramus must draw a sword to kill himself.

So write me a prologue to say Pyramus is not really dead.

Also, a lion among ladies is a dreadful thing.

So let's have Snug tell the audience that he is not a real lion.

In search of Titania, Puck stumbles upon the actors.

A play?! I'll watch!

You stay here. I shall return soon.

I've never seen a stranger actor.

He's one I'd like to play a trick on!

In another part of the forest . . .

Have you done what I asked, Puck?

Titania awoke and fell in love with an ass!

And the Athenian?

Yes, Lord. I streaked his eyes with juice.

This is the same Athenian?

This is the woman, but this is not the man . . .

Soon, Puck returns, followed by Lysander and Helena . . .

Helena is here, and so is the Athenian youth on whom I used the juice by mistake.

The two youths awaken.

Lord, what fools these mortals be!

Why do you think that I'm teasing you, Helena?

Your love belongs to Hermia.

48

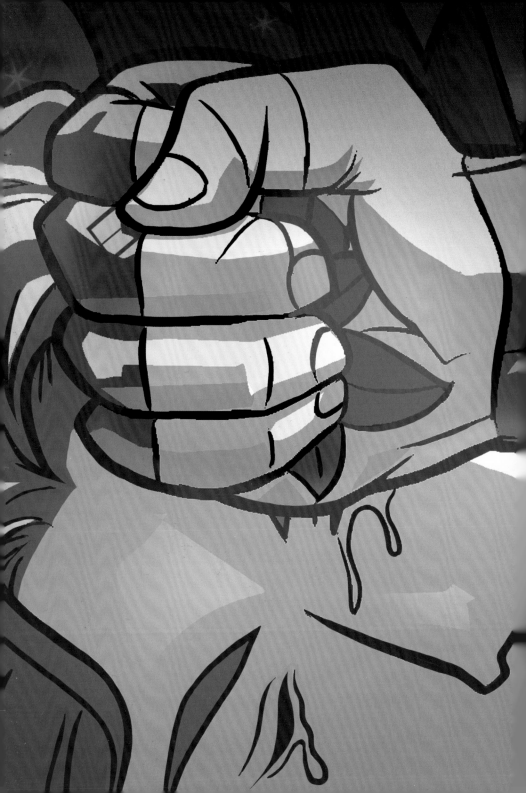

ACT FOUR

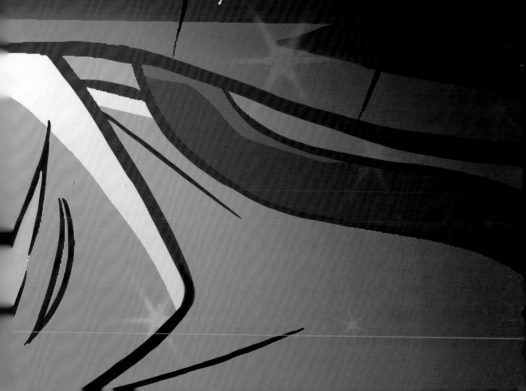

"I have had a dream, past the wit of man to say what dream it was."

ACT FIVE

"If we shadows have offended,
think but this, and all is mended,
that you have but slumber'd here
while these visions did appear."

Now, what entertainment shall we have?

Here is a list of plays the actors can perform, Your Highness.

A sad comedy? That doesn't make much sense.

But let's see it!

"*Pyramus and Thisbe* – a very sad and tragic comedy."

Before the play begins . . .

Ladies and gentlemen, perhaps you are wondering who the characters in this play will be.

Please allow me to introduce them!

This scary beast is named Lion!
I wonder if the lion will talk.
If these donkeys can speak, then a lion should be able to.
I am a Wall that has a hole, through which the lovers whisper in secret.
The wall talks, too!
It is the cleverest wall that I've ever heard!

ABOUT THE RETELLING AUTHOR

The career path of **Nel Yomtov** has taken him from the halls of Marvel Comics, as an editor, writer, and colourist, to the world of toy development. He then became editorial and art director at a children's non-fiction book publisher, and now Nel is a writer and editor of books, websites, and comics for children. A harmonica-honking blues enthusiast, Nel lives with his wife, Nancy. They have a son, Jess.

ABOUT THE ILLUSTRATORS

Berenice Muniz is a graphic designer and illustrator from Monterrey, Mexico. In the past, she has done work for publicity agencies and art exhibitions, and she's even created her own webcomic. These days, Berenice is devoted to illustrating comics. In her spare time, "Bere" loves to draw, read manga, watch animated films, play video games, and kill zombies.

Fares Maese is a graphic designer and illustrator. He has worked as a colourist for Marvel Comics and as a concept artist for the card and role-playing games Pathfinder and Warhammer. Fares loves spending time playing video games and he's a brilliant drum player.

ABOUT
WILLIAM SHAKESPEARE

William Shakespeare's true date of birth is unknown, but it is celebrated on 23 April 1564. He was born in Stratford-upon-Avon in Warwickshire and was the third of eight children to his parents, John and Mary.

At the age of 18, William married a woman named Anne Hathaway on 27 November 1582. He and Anne had three children together, including twins. After that point, Shakespeare's history is somewhat of a mystery. Not much is known about this period of his life, until 1592 when his plays first graced theatre stages in London.

From 1594 onwards, Shakespeare performed his plays with a stage company called the Lord Chamberlain's Men (later known as the King's Men). They soon became the top playing company in all of London, earning the favour of Queen Elizabeth I and King James I along the way.

Shakespeare retired in 1613, and died at the age of 52 on 23 April 1616. He was buried at Holy Trinity Church in Stratford. The epitaph on his grave curses any person who disturbs it. Translated to modern English, part of it reads:

> *Blessed be the man that spares these stones,*
> *And cursed be he who moves my bones.*

Over a period of 25 years, Shakespeare wrote more than 40 works, including poems, plays, and prose. His plays have been performed all over the world and translated into every major language.

THE HISTORY BEHIND THE PLAY

Shakespeare was inspired by many other works when he wrote *A Midsummer Night's Dream*. For example, the story of Pyramus and Thisbe, from Ovid's *Metamorphoses*, played an important role in the creation of Shakespeare's play. It served as a basis for several parts of the play's plot, and is even included in *A Midsummer Night's Dream* as a play-within-a-play! *Pyramus and Thisbe* was also an inspiration for *Romeo and Juliet*, another of Shakespeare's most popular plays.

Greek mythology served as a basis for several of the character's names in *A Midsummer Night's Dream*. In ancient Greek myths, Lysander was a mythological Greek warlord, Theseus was the King of Athens, and Hippolyta was the Queen of the Amazons – a race of fierce, female warriors.

While *A Midsummer Night's Dream* had many inspirations, it has also influenced modern culture. For example, when William Herschel, a British astronomer, discovered the two moons circling the planet Uranus in 1787, he named them Oberon and Titania in honour of the king and queen of the fairies.

No one knows for certain when *A Midsummer Night's Dream* was first written or performed. Nevertheless, the play has been performed across the globe for hundreds of years. It has also been recreated as musicals, operas, ballets, books, films – and graphic novels like this one.

SHAKESPEAREAN LANGUAGE

Shakespeare's writing is powerful and memorable – and sometimes difficult to understand. Many lines in his plays can be read in different ways or can have multiple meanings. Also, English spelling and pronunciation have changed over time, so the way he spelled words was not always the same as the way we spell them now. However, Shakespeare still influences the way we write and speak today. Below are some of his more famous phrases that have also become part of our language.

FAMOUS LINES FROM A MIDSUMMER NIGHT'S DREAM

"The course of true love never did run smooth." (Act I, Scene I)

SPEAKER: Lysander
MODERN INTERPRETATION: **True love always faces obstacles.**
EXPLANATION: Lysander explains to Hermia that being in love is always difficult because so many things have to be considered when two lovers want to be together.

"I am that merry wanderer of the night." (Act II, Scene I)

SPEAKER: Puck (Robin Goodfellow)
MODERN INTERPRETATION: **That's me, I am the playful Robin Goodfellow, also known as Puck.**
EXPLANATION: Puck, a playful fairy-sprite, plays tricks on others on Oberon's behalf. Puck identifies himself formally as Robin Goodfellow, but most fairies know him simply as Puck.

"And yet, to say the truth, reason and love keep little company together nowadays." (Act III, Scene I)

SPEAKER: Bottom

MODERN INTERPRETATION: **To tell you the truth, logic and love rarely go hand in hand these days.**

EXPLANATION: Titania, under a spell, falls in love with Bottom at first sight. Bottom, not knowing he has the head of a donkey, remarks that she has no reason to love him. He then adds that, lately, love hasn't been making much sense at all.

"I have had a dream, past the wit of man to say what dream it was." (Act IV, Scene I)

SPEAKER: Bottom

MODERN INTERPRETATION: **I was dreaming! My dream was so strange that I couldn't even explain it if I tried.**

EXPLANATION: Bottom thinks that the entire experience of falling in love with Titania was only a dream.

"If we shadows have offended, think but this, and all is mended, that you have but slumber'd here while these visions did appear." (Act V, Scene I)

SPEAKER: Puck

MODERN INTERPRETATION: **If you, the viewer, did not like anything that happened in this play, then relax – it was all just your dream.**

EXPLANATION: Puck breaks the "fourth wall" and speaks directly to the audience of the play. He tells them that they should not worry if they were offended, or they did not like what they saw during the play, because they only dreamt the whole thing.

DISCUSSION QUESTIONS

1. Of all the characters in *A Midsummer Night's Dream*, which one was your favourite? Why?

2. This play is considered to be a comedy. Did you think it was funny? Why or why not?

3. Do think Theseus was a fair ruler in this book? What about King Oberon? What makes for a good ruler?

WRITING PROMPTS

1. Magic and spells are used to distract, confuse, and control characters in this book. Think up a magic spell of your own. What does it do? How do you cast it? Write about your spell. Then draw a picture of your spell in action.

2. In the play, Oberon and Titania fight over an Indian boy. In Shakespeare's time, fairies were said to steal children and keep them as servants. Imagine that you are kidnapped by fairies for a day. Write about your experiences as the son or daughter of a fairy king and queen.

3. The performance of *Pyramus and Thisbe* in *A Midsummer Night's Dream* is called a play-within-a-play. Write your own one-page play, including several characters, a story, and dialogue.

TRODUCING SHAKESPEARE'S
MACBETH
Late that night . . .
What
f we fail in
our task?
But screw your courage to the sticking-place, and we'll not fail.
Drugged wine has put the king's guards into a deep sleep.
Is . . . is this a dagger I see before me?!
Or have I simply lost my mind . . . ?